THE HAUNTING OF EQUESTRIA

An Adventure for **Tails of EQUESTRIA**

Contents

Credits

Written by: Andrew Peregrine

Cover Art: Tony Fleecs

Internal Art: Chris Cæsar, Emy Clark, Anna Semp & Hasbro Studios

Book Layout & Graphic Design: Chris Cæsar

Produced & Edited By: Zak Barouh & Alessio Cavatore

Proofreading by: Mark Pollard

Thanks to: Libby Welham, Heather Hopkins, Marion Bardou, Hugo Pritchard-Law, Criz Jamers, and Princess Luna

ISBN: 978-0-9932184-4-6

Product Code: RH_TOE_012

Published by Shinobi 7 in the United States and Canada.

She could smell their fear. Those small foals had been so easy to scare it almost wasn't any fun. Almost. Even though the dungeons were far below the throne room, she could feel their panic through the stone of her castle and it made her smile. They had been so easy to capture, wandering across the black plain in those outlandish costumes. At least it proved they weren't spies. Her enemies were far too clever for that, unless...

Walking over to the balcony she looked out over the land. She stared in pride at the blasted forest and the plains of darkness, the ruins of Ponyville. She listened in wonder at the howls of the tormented spirits that swept across the sunless sky. All was dark, all was peaceful.

But she had to remain on her guard. Even though she had finally defeated her sister, there were always rebels looking to fight against her rule. She would root them out from the shadows, her shadows, and destroy them all. She was Princess Argent, the Queen of Fear, and none would stand before her.

So if they weren't spies, where had the foals come from? They didn't even know who she was. They had called her 'Nightmare Moon.' Who was that, she wondered? It was certainly someone they were frightened of, that much was certain. She reached out with her mind, following the shimmering paths of dark magic that threaded the land like a vast spider web. Yes, there was something else there. Over in the distance, powerful magic had been woken up. Down there, among the broken houses of Ponyville something shone with sorcery.

It was a door, it had to be, a doorway that those foolish foals had stumbled through. She felt fear from the other side, a fear she could use, dread that would keep the door open. But there was a dangerous joy there too. A sickening feeling of friendship also emanated from the portal. It drew the spirits and the weaker minds toward it. Such things were a threat. She would have to make the first strike, have to subjugate this other land before it corrupted everything she had built.

Yes, that was it. She would gather her soldiers and the darkest spirits and invade this new realm, claiming it for herself. Maybe there she would find the key to transform into a true mistress of the dark arts. Then nothing would ever dare to challenge her again. This new world would be hers. What had those foals called it? Ah yes, Equestria...

Introduction

Equestria is a wondrous and magical place, but magic can be used for darkness as well as light. In this adventure the PCs discover a whole new world, but one shadowed in darkness and fear. They will have to use the power of light and friendship to defeat the frightening spirits and shadows they are about to face.

This is an adventure module for My Little Pony: Tails of Equestria. It is intended to run as a standalone adventure. But it can be easily played after or before other adventures like The Curse of the Statuettes and The Festival of Lights. It is advised that you run The Pet Predicament from the Core Rulebook to familiarize yourself with the rules first, but you can dive straight into this one if you prefer.

The story begins with the PCs celebrating Nightmare Night. As they enjoy the festivities, they discover some of the hauntings are actually real and discover strange creatures are abroad in Ponyville. Finding a portal to another realm, they find themselves facing an alternate version of a dark Princess Luna. If they can face her they may be able to close the portal before she invades Equestria!

This adventure is a spooky tale rather than an action adventure. While the characters may be very scared at certain points, the players will hopefully not be. They will face several forms of spirits that appear to be ghosts. But they are actually just new creatures rather than lost souls. It also brings a new 'Shadow Realm' to the world of Equestria, creating potential for extra adventures. This realm is a strange reverse of the world the PCs know, ruled by 'The Queen of Fear.'

As there are a lot of scary monsters in this adventure, we also add some optional rules to reflect how frightened the PCs are getting. The game master is free not to use these rules and rely on the players to play out their character's fears. But this system provides a helpful way to keep track of how any scary things each character has been affected by.

This adventure should suit PCs of levels 5-10, as a group of beginning characters may find it rather difficult. If the adventure does prove too much or too little of a challenge, the game master can adjust some of the difficulty levels and trait dice of the opposition.

In some cases you might want to see who finds a particular clue. At such times every PC in the scene should make a roll, but the game master should then only give the clue to the PC with the highest result. After all, friends should tell each other what they know! But it is also important to make sure that every character gets the chance to be in the spotlight and contribute to the group. So it is good to encourage a shy player to be the one to make an important roll for the group, and remember not to listen only to the loudest player during the game.

This book is intended for you – the game master – to tell another exciting tale in the world of Equestria. As such you should feel free to adapt it to the style of play your group prefers. The adventure overview will give you the outline of the adventure, but you should add your own personal flavor to the encounters as you play through. You can also adapt the difficulty of the adventure to suit the PCs' skills, and swap out similar NPCs with characters they have met in previous adventures. But if this is your first time running a game, you should find everything you need is here for you to play it straight through.

As usual, the only golden rule is that everyone should have fun, and tell an entertaining, and spooky, tale with your friends.

Overview

Many years ago, as a young student of magic, Princess Celestia used to study with the great wizard Star Swirl the Bearded. Celestia proved an apt student and became more of a partner as they delved together into the secrets and mysteries of the universe. In their studies they discovered a way to visit whole new worlds. By enchanting mirrors, they created portals to other versions of Equestria. Together, they adventured across these other realms and the strange and unique cultures they came across.

Some of these worlds were almost the same as Equestria, with only a few minor changes. Ponyville might have a different name, or the trains were a different color. But most realms were very different. Some existed in another era, such as an ice age or the Wild West. Others had undergone very different choices, such as places where Celestia and Luna were the bad guys.

The wonders of these new worlds proved extremely tempting and addictive. Celestia became too involved in one in particular and Star Swirl the Bearded realized that sooner or later they would come across somewhere dangerous. They shut down their experiments, destroying most of the enchanted mirrors and hiding the spells that could create more.

But not all the mirrors were destroyed, and one that led to a very dangerous world went missing. While Celestia and Star Swirl believed this mirror to be no longer enchanted, some of the magic remained, waiting for the right circumstances to awaken its power once more.

Many years later, the present day, it is Nightmare Night once again. However, a foal called Summer is not enjoying the festivities. Having read too much about how frightening Nightmare Moon was, she has scared herself silly. This fear, and the power of Nightmare Night itself has woken up the ancient mirror, that has now become the centerpiece of one of Ponyville's 'haunted houses.' Several strange ghostly spirits have already come through from the 'Shadow Realm' but a few foals have also wandered through themselves, thinking it is all part of the show.

The first the PCs will know about what is going on is when they find out some of the ghostly sightings around the town are not just pranks. Luckily, the spirits they find are actually as lost and frightened as they are frightening. With a little care and consideration, the PCs can calm down the spirits and learn a little more about where they came from.

Once the PCs know where the spirits originated, they can make their way to the haunted house. There, they discover the foals have gone missing and they enter the Shadow Realm to rescue them. In this ghostly place they have to face Princess Argent, who rules the place as 'The Queen of Fear.' But there is help at hand in the shape of a resistance movement called 'The Hooves of Light.'

Returning to Ponyville with the foals, the PCs discover the portal is resisting all attempts to close it. A furious Princess Argent decides to invade Equestria to learn the secrets of Nightmare Moon. She readies a great army, but cannot cross the portal, yet. However, even the Mane Six cannot close the portal as Summer's fear is keeping it open! Can the PCs escape the clutches of Princess Argent, rescue the foals, help Summer find her courage, and close the portal before a new reign of darkness sweeps Equestria?

Characters

Princess Argent — The Queen of Fear

In the Shadow Realm, the battle between Princess Celestia and Nightmare Moon did not go so well. Princess Argent (Luna) won the battle and banished Princess Solar (Celestia) from the land, rebuilding the realm as a place of shadow and darkness. She took the name 'The Queen of Fear' and ruled the realm with terror; her subjects turned to shadow and never learned the wonder of the Elements of Harmony.

However, she could not quite make the change to become a true mistress of darkness as Nightmare Moon did. This would require her to create her own version of Nightmare Moon's Helm of Shadows. So when she hears that Equestria's Luna managed that feat, Argent decides to invade and claim the helmet to allow her to finally become Nightmare Moon, a true queen of darkness.

Princess Solar

After many years, the Shadow Realm's version of Celestia, Princess Solar has managed to return. She is still weak but has formed a resistance movement against the Queen of Fear. Calling themselves the 'Hooves of Light,' they do their best to free those they can from the yoke of Argent's rule. She and her movement will prove a powerful ally to the PCs, and they may want to help her one day overthrow the Queen of Fear. Princess Solar is as noble and kind as Princess Celestia, but not as powerful or skilled. She is still recovering from her long battle with her sister. She is more of a Robin Hood figure than a noble Queen.

Summer

This young foal is the unwitting source of the problems. She was reading a book on the old stories of Princess Luna as Nightmare Moon and got very scared. Her fear, coupled with it being Nightmare Night, was enough to reopen an old portal to the Shadow Realm. While Princess Argent used her magic to open it further, it cannot be closed while Summer remains afraid. The only way to break her fear is to face Princess Argent, something she will need a lot of help to do!

Trick or Treaters

The PCs will initially be in charge of a group of young foals. There will be quite a variety of them and some will be trouble where others might be helpful. Summer is technically one of them, but she will be too scared to come out. The players should take a hand in helping the game master create these characters who might prove useful allies, highly troublesome, or even both!

Dark Shadow

Dark Shadow was originally named 'Candy Flair' until he got his cutie mark and took on a much more dramatic persona. He now dresses only in black and lets his long mane hang over his face all the time. He can be rather tedious to talk to, only ever discussing rather depressing subjects and 'the essential ennui of existence.' However, he is a very good poet and while his late night 'poetry jam' sessions can be a little depressing, they are also full of talent. Each year he organizes a haunted house for Nightmare Night which he enjoys doing immensely even though he'd never admit to getting excited about anything!

Rainbow Tie

Rainbow Tie is an Earth Pony who runs the fashionable clothing boutique 'Canter Klein.' While his clothes are expensive, they are very well made and Rainbow numbers Rarity among his regular customers. However, he doesn't just sell clothes. He offers fashion advice to all his customers and never lets anyone leave his shop looking anything but their best (as far as he is concerned!).

Commander Daring

The unit commander is one of Princess Solar's most trusted lieutenants. Daring has proved herself in several conflicts but always makes the safety of her unit her priority. Like her soldiers, she is very serious, but she really wants to be able to laugh. She just doesn't think it would be appropriate in front of her troops. But if someone can get her to really laugh, she will remember what she is truly fighting for and trust the PCs a lot more easily.

Fear Points
New Optional Rule

Pony adventurers are usually brave and true, but in this adventure, a lot of scary things happen to the PCs. It may be enough to test even the most stalwart pony. But it is important to remember that being brave is not about never being afraid. The bravest people are very frightened, but they are able to overcome it and not let it get the better of them.

So, when the PCs meet ghosts and spirits and face frightening adversaries in a spooky new world, it is bound to have an effect on them! In general, it is best for the players to play their characters as they feel they would be affected by what they encounter. However, to represent the gradual build-up of dread they might feel as the adventure progresses, we offer a system you can use if you prefer.

Whenever a PC sees something that might frighten them, they can make a Mind test to see if it really scares them. This is called a 'fear test.' The Difficulty of the roll depends on how frightening it is. Somepony jumping out at you and saying 'boo' will only be Difficulty 2, but facing an enraged Nightmare Moon will be Difficulty 20! If the test is failed, the character gets a fear point. If they roll a 1, not only do they get a fear point but they have a big scare. They will attempt to run away or hide until the source of the fear is gone. In some cases the game master might declare that what they experienced is so scary, they automatically gain a fear point.

The more fear points you have, the more frightened and nervous your pony becomes. For each three fear points you have, you must pick one of your traits. So, if at 3 points you pick one trait, you pick a second one at 6 fear points, and another at 9 fear points, you will have picked all three! When you make a test using a picked trait, you downgrade your die and use the next lowest one instead. So, if you have D6 you roll a D4 instead. If your trait is only a D4, you can't downgrade it any more.

The reason for this depends on the trait you have picked. If it is Body, your knees are shaking so much you have trouble coordinating. If it is Mind, you are so preoccupied with what you are feeling you aren't thinking straight. If you picked Charm, you have become so frightened you can't look anyone in the eye or talk without stuttering.

How do you get rid of fear points? There are two ways to do this. The first is to roll an Exploding Hooves result (when your die rolls its maximum, which lets you immediately roll an upgraded die as well). Such a burst of confidence, especially if you are facing something scary, is enough to make you feel a bit better. You can remove 1 fear point just for getting an Exploding Hooves, but the game master might allow you to remove a second fear point as well if you were standing up to your fear in some way.

The second way to remove fear is from the help and support of your friends. Anypony can spend some time talking to you and telling you how they will do their best to keep you safe and support you. If they do this and spend a Friendship point, you can reduce your fear points by 1. Otherwise fear points vanish at the end of an adventure when the character has had time to rest and recuperate from their scary adventures.

Telling Spooky Stories

This adventure takes the PCs into some very dark places. In the Shadow Realm, evil rules with an iron hand and Princess Argent has done dreadful things to maintain her power. For the PCs it will be rather scary, but it is important to make sure it doesn't give the players nightmares too!

It can be a lot of fun to be scared. We scream and shout when a scary thing happens and laugh about how silly we felt when it turns out we are safe after all. When our characters get scared, we can have fun describing how they do silly things to run away or how they panic and try to hide. We can enjoy the shock and surprise because we know we are really safe and playing a game with friends.

It can be good to emphasize the nasty things Princess Argent has done and how she treats her subjects poorly. Such things will motivate the PCs to make sure she doesn't win. But at the same time, few people and creatures in Equestria are completely evil. Most still have at least some spark of goodness inside them if it can only be reawakened. If Nightmare Moon can be returned to the side of good, there is hope for everyone.

So it is important not to focus too much on how scary anything might be. This adventure should be like going into a fairground haunted house. Exciting and fun, and a little bit scary, but never really frightening. The game master should make sure everyone is having fun and if someone is feeling a little bit scared, they should respect their feelings. They should stop the scene, and just explain how the scene plays out without going into any more detail. Then you move onto the next scene.

Having said that, this adventure is an opportunity to have the fun of Halloween any day of the year! You might find some horror themed biscuits and candy for everyone while you play. Perhaps dim the lights and put on some spooky music or sound effects to help set the scene. Remember, the important thing is to ensure everyone is having fun and enjoying the game.

Nightmare Moon

"Oh, my beloved subjects. It's been so long since I've seen your precious little sun-loving faces."
- Nightmare Moon

As this adventure takes place during Nightmare Night, we should tell you a little about that before we go any further! Nightmare Night is a very important celebration in Equestria, and traces its origins back to when Princess Luna was Nightmare Moon. According to legend, Princess Celestia's sister, Princess Luna, was once corrupted by her jealousy. It turned her into a terrible being called Nightmare Moon and for many years she frightened the ponies of Equestria.

In old legend it was said that once a year, in the days of Nightmare Moon, she would swoop out of the sky and gobble up any pony she found. So, on that night, ponies dressed up in costume to confuse Nightmare Moon. Another part of the tradition is collecting candy, so if anypony meets Nightmare Moon they have something to offer her. If she gets full up with candy then she won't have room to eat anypony!

While many years ago, Princess Luna did become Nightmare Moon (and was every bit as frightening), she was recently brought back to herself by the Mane Six and the Elements of Harmony. However, everyone loves Nightmare Night so much that the celebration has continued. Princess Luna has even been known to join in the fun and pretend to be Nightmare Moon for the night to bring a few more entertaining scares. During the festival, foals dress up in costume and go around the neighborhood collecting candy. Everyone joins in the celebrations and there are plenty of pranks and games to entertain everyone (who all get to stay up really late too!).

A little known fact about Princess Luna's transformation into Nightmare Moon, was that it created a powerful artifact called 'The Helm of Shadows.' This magical helm was crafted from Nightmare Moon's turbulent emotions and was the source of much of her dark power. The helm was too powerful to be destroyed, even after Princess Luna returned. So Luna and Celestia buried it in a secure place in Everfree forest. Should anyone find and claim the helm, they could take on the powers of Nightmare Moon and bring a new dark age to Equestria.

Adventure Summary

Nightmare Night (Page 14)
The PCs get ready for Nightmare Night, sorting out their costumes and collecting the foals they will be looking after for the evening.

Things that go Bump (Page 20)
As the PCs trick or treat and play games during the celebrations, they discover some of the spooky hauntings are actually real! They need to stop several spirits scaring the locals and damaging property. If they make friends with the spirits they can gather clues about where they have come from.

The Haunted Mansion (Page 26)
The spirit's clues lead the PCs to a haunted house in the middle of Ponyville. It has been set up for pranks and scary tricks, but it turns out some of them are real. In the center of the house is a huge mirror, which has become a portal to another world, where the spirits are coming from. Unfortunately, a group of foals visiting the house thought the portal was all part of the show and went through.

The Shadow Realm (Page 30)
The PCs go through the mirror portal to rescue the foals. They find themselves in a shadow version of Equestria, where this version of Princess Luna defeated Princess Celestia when they fought, but couldn't quite become Nightmare Moon. The land is a place of darkness and shadow, full of scary spirits and tormented souls.

The Hooves of Light (Page 36)
Looking for the lost foals, the PCs run into a group called 'The Hooves of Light.' These resistance fighters are led by Princess Solar, this realm's version of Princess Celestia. Once the PCs can convince them they are friends, the Hooves of Light will help them look for the lost foals.

The Castle of Fear (Page 44)
The foals are being held in Princess Argent's huge castle of shadows. Using a secret tunnel known to the Hooves of Light, the PCs can get inside and rescue the foals. They discover that Princess Argent is also known as the Queen of Fear for a good reason. She draws power from the fear others feel and has grown stronger by terrifying the foals.

Shadow Busters (Page 52)
Returning to Equestria the PCs want to find a way to close the portal, but even Twilight Sparkle can't manage to do it. It appears something is keeping it open from the Equestria side. At the same time, Princess Argent sends huge shadow spirits through the portal to invade Equestria. Luckily, Twilight Sparkle has created some anti-spirit weapons that utilize the Elements of Harmony. The PCs arm themselves and join the battle for Ponyville against the creatures of shadow.

Facing Fear (Page 57)
As they fight the shadow spirits, the PCs discover the source of what is keeping the portal open. Summer has been reading about Nightmare Moon and scared herself enough to make a connection to the shadow realm. The PCs need to help her face and overcome her fears. They travel through the portal once more to face Princess Argent!

Nightmare Night

"Remember this day little ponies, for it was your last.
From this moment forth, the night will last forever!"
- Nightmare Moon

Read Aloud:

It is Nightmare Night in Ponyville once again, the yearly celebration where everypony dresses up in a costume to confuse Nightmare Moon, should she return to gobble everyone up! It is a time of candy and games and spooky stories. As night falls the real festivities get underway and crowds of ponies take to the streets to trick or treat around the neighborhood.

The whole town is decorated in a spooky theme. Fake spider webs hang from the street lanterns and everything is lit in shades of blue and green. Everypony is laughing and enjoying themselves, but there is something in the air. Maybe it is the excitement, maybe the fear that Nightmare Moon might actually visit, maybe the occasional prank has some ponies on edge. But you all feel there is going to be something more to tonight, something dark, something dangerous...

Nightmare Night is once again in full swing in Ponyville. This yearly festival used to be a reminder that Nightmare Moon might return to terrorize Equestria. But these days, with Princess Luna returned by the Elements of Harmony, it is a time to play spooky games and maybe scare yourself just a little bit for fun.

The game master should begin by asking the PCs how they are celebrating the night. What are they most excited about? Do they look forward to getting candy from their neighbors or do they enjoy giving it out? Are they going to play pranks on anypony? If so, who and what do they intend to do? Might they most look forward to playing games like bobbing for apples or throwing spiders onto webs? Everyone should have a favorite part of Nightmare Night which they should all take a moment to share with the group.

Fancy Dress

The other important part of Nightmare Night is the costumes! Pretty much everypony loves to dress up on a night like this, but what sort of costume are they going to pick? There are plenty of options to choose from:

★ **Animal:** They might just dress as a creature, like a dog or cat, or something weird like an octopus! They might even be something more supernatural, like a dragon or a gryphon.

★ **Famous pony:** Like Twilight Sparkle they might want to go as Star Swirl the Bearded, or even Princess Celestia, Nightmare Moon, or one of the Mane Six.

★ **Profession:** There are plenty of options for being a pirate, inventor, fire fighter, explorer, or even a ninja.

★ **Scary creature:** If they want to be spooky they could be a vampire, mummy, scarecrow, or witch.

Once each character has picked a costume, they should describe it to the rest of the group. What color is the outfit? How easily can people guess what it is? Is it expensive and well made or a little thrown together? Did the character take time to get their costume perfect or just grab something at the last minute?

It is possible that not all the characters will really enjoy Nightmare Night. If so, they should tell the group why they are not participating. Do they find it a little too scary? Maybe they think the costumes are silly. Perhaps someone played a mean prank on them one year and it spoiled the celebration for them. Perhaps they just enjoy spending time alone while everypony else is out.

Getting Ready

No matter how involved each of the characters has chosen to be, they will have to be out and about this year. Each of them has agreed to take some of the younger foals trick or treating. It is up to each PC how happy they are about this! They might be looking forward to collecting candy themselves, or feel the whole thing is a chore they have to do before they can have some fun. However, it is up to them how they organize the evening together. They might take one foal each around the town, or all join together in a large group to go trick or treating together.

Each of the PCs has one foal they are responsible for. They can detail this foal themselves, ask the game master to do so for them, or perhaps be looking after one of the Cutie Mark Crusaders or another personality of Ponyville. Each foal has the same statistics, but more importantly they should be given a personality quirk so the game master can play them as a character. These uirks should be picked to cause the PCs some trouble! Any of the quirks in the book might apply.

Slow
The foal is always lagging behind and the last to leave anywhere. The PCs have to keep an eye out not to lose them.

Prankster
This foal likes to play pranks, such as throwing water balloons or using magic to cause trouble. Some people will find this funny; other people won't enjoy them at all!

Candy Obsessed
This foal wants CANDY!! They will be looking to get the most and even take more than their fair share. They will dash toward any offer of candy as fast as possible.

Expert
This foal has read a lot and insists on explaining anything that anypony mentions. They will want to hold up the whole group to point out interesting buildings in Ponyville or places the Mane Six have had adventures.

Role Player
This foal has taken their costume very seriously. They are playing the part to the hilt, refusing to break character for any reason. An inventor will ramble on about her new design; a crocodile will want to bite everyone.

Shy
This foal wants to take part but is really nervous of saying anything, or pushing forward to get candy from any houses. If the PCs fail to notice them hanging back they will end the evening with no candy at all.

Over Excited
This foal is the opposite of slow and shy, and stays at the forefront of everything. In fact, it will be hard to get them to slow down and stay with the group rather than run off toward anything shiny or interesting.

Earth Pony foal

Body: D6   **Mind: D4**   **Charm: D6**   **Stamina: 10**

Talents: Stout Heart (D4)

Pegasus foal

Body: D4   **Mind: D4**   **Charm: D6**   **Stamina: 8**

Talents: Fly (D4)

Unicorn foal

Body: D4   **Mind: D4**   **Charm: D6**   **Stamina: 8**

Talents: Telekinesis (D4)

Trick or Treat?

Whether the PCs take their foals around Ponyville individually, or as a group, they will find their foal will get them into difficulties at some point, depending on their personality. It will take Mind rolls (Difficulty 4) to keep an eye on them, and Body rolls (Difficulty 4) to catch any of them that run off. Those that need a talking to will only behave on a Charm roll (Difficulty 4). The game master should have some fun making the experience of chaperoning the foals quite difficult, but not so hard it spoils Nightmare Night.

There is one foal missing though, and that is Summer. She is on the list of foals the PCs are meant to be looking after, but some of the other foals will say they know she isn't coming. She was last seen going to the library saying she didn't want to come out. The PCs might go to the library to find her, and if they do they will discover her there reading a book. She will refuse to join the group, and on a Mind roll (Difficulty 5) they will notice she seems very scared about the whole celebration. As she is safe and sound in the library the best thing is to leave her be. If they force her to join them she will simply slip away back to the library at any and every opportunity.

Candy Total

Another tradition of trick or treating is a little competition over who can get the most candy! Each of the PC's foals gets to roll their Charm (D6) three times over the evening as they visit houses, and each result adds to a pool of 'Candy Points' for each of them. The PCs can help twice using one of their own Traits.

Body: For getting around quickly and visiting more houses in the time available.

Mind: For figuring out which houses are giving out the most candy.

Charm: For convincing each place to give them just a little more candy for being adorable.

These rolls might be done at any point over the evening, as the PCs deal with ghosts and other fun and games. At the end of the evening (or even the adventure) each foal's total of Candy Points represent how much they have collected, the highest being the winner. If any PCs suggest those with the most share a little with those who have the least, they should get a friendship point. But it will take a Charm roll (Difficulty 4) to get any of the foals to part with any candy!

The game master might like to have some real candy at hand, and offer it to the players in the order of who got the most points (but do make sure everyone gets something)!

Fun & Games

The celebrations for Nightmare Night don't just involve candy! As well as trick or treating, the PCs can get involved in several games that are set up across the town. They might compete against other ponies, each other, or even one of the Mane Six for the most points. An especially good win might earn them a prize at the game master's discretion.

Spider Throwing

The pony has to throw a toy spider at a web target, aiming to get closest to the middle. This is a Body test with a Difficulty of 3, but the highest roll each round from the participants is the winner.

Apple Bobbing

This game involves trying to get apples out of a bucket of water with only your mouth. It is a Body test (Difficulty 4) to get an apple at all, but the highest roll gets the most apples in the limited time.

Decorations

The streets are still being decorated in the early hours of the festival. Anypony is allowed to help add streamers, balloons and garlands around the area. Making a good display is a difficulty 4 Charm roll, and the higher the roll the better the decorations look.

Shock scares

Some ponies are playing pranks by trying to scare each other. Anyone trying to do so must make an opposed Mind roll against their chosen victim. If the prankster rolls highest they give their target a scare. If the target rolls a 1 the scare is bad enough to earn them a fear point!

Things That Go Bump

"It's the horrifying story of the messy, inconsiderate ghost who irritated everypony within a hundred miles."

- Rarity

As the PCs wander the town trick or treating, they are about to realize that some of the ghostly encounters are more than just pranks. Tonight, Ponyville is actually haunted! Several ghostly spirits have found their way from another world and are causing havoc around the town. While not every home is full of spirits, plenty are causing mayhem across the town. These spirits aren't actually ghosts, but a peculier magical creature from the Realm of Shadows.

While the spirits initially appear quite frightening, they are mostly just upset and frustrated. If the PCs can get to the root of what is bothering them, they can end the haunting and make friends with the spirit. Each spirit has trouble remembering how they got into Equestria, but they all remember something about their journey. If the PCs can put these clues together, they can find out where they are all coming from. All the spirits would like to return home, but don't quite know where that is. Traveling between worlds has left them all a bit befuddled. If the PCs can figure it out, they will all happily leave.

The game master should use the following encounters between any other events and encounters going on during the Nightmare Night celebrations. They can go in any order and either follow each other or alternate with more mundane adventures.

Spirits

Body: D4	Mind: D6	Charm: D6	Stamina: 10

Talents: Insubstantial (D12), Magic Resistance (D8), spirits may have extra powers detailed in their encounter

Quirks: Upset, Unliving

Grumpy Phantom

At the end of one of the darker roads in Ponyville is an abandoned house. It wasn't a particularly spooky place, but tonight it has taken on a more menacing appearance. Several foals are daring each other to go in, and the nerves and excitement when any of them do, has got them all screaming and giggling.

However, as the PCs come by, they see a couple of foals run screaming out of the house. They stutter that there really is a ghost in there! As if to answer them, a low angry moan issues from the house and the door slams shut.

The foals will look expectantly at the PCs to investigate. But if they don't the foals will do a quick head count and discover one of their number (a filly called Sparkle Shower) is still inside and may need rescuing!

Inside, the house is dark and spooky. While the place is structurally safe and secure, it has no power or light, and no furniture either. Any PCs making a Mind test (Difficulty 4) will notice Sparkle Shower cowering in a cupboard in one of the upstairs bedrooms. But once they find her, the spirit appears!

The spirit is a large white shape with a long beard and a walking cane. He moves very slowly and as soon as he appears he shouts "leave this place" in a loud booming voice, waving his stick in the air. The PCs should all make a Mind test (Difficulty 4). Those who fail gain a fear point and get very scared, possibly running away if no one stops them. If they return and face the ghost they need to make the same test but at Difficulty 3.

Those who stand firm and can face the ghost will be roared at with his hideous moan. He will shout that they should not only leave but get those foals outside off his lawn! If they talk to him it becomes clear he thinks this is his house as he recognizes the wallpaper. He is only angry because he thinks all these ponies are rudely walking into his house! A Charm test from the PCs may get him to calm down, but an offer of tea and a sit down will do the job just as well.

Once he is calm, the spirit will realize this isn't actually his house, mainly as all his things aren't here. He'll apologize as he is getting on a bit and his memory is going. He will tell the PCs he doesn't remember much about getting here, but that he passed through some sort of mirror and arrived here.

Poltergeist

As the PCs pass a clothes boutique, a well-dressed pony called Rainbow Tie will come running out in terror. He will throw himself at the PCs and desperately ask them to help save his shop! From inside the place the PCs can hear crashes and bangs as it seems the whole place is being turned upside down.

Entering the shop, the PCs will see everything is a mess. Racks and rails have been thrown around and clothes lie everywhere. In the center of the shop is a whirlwind of clothes, bags, and shoes, screaming in rage (and the PCs should make a fear test (Mind) at Difficulty 4 not to get a fear point). These items will be thrown at the PCs as soon as they enter, doing a point of Stamina damage to anyone who fails a Body test (Difficulty 6). Each round the PCs are in the shop, the poltergeist will throw something at one of them until they can calm it down.

If the PCs investigate the piles of clothes (while trying to take cover!) they can make a Mind test (Difficulty 4) to notice there is a color pattern to how they have been thrown around. Particular colors of items have clearly been put together. If they decide to help organize more of the strewn items into this pattern, the poltergeist will begin to calm down. It takes a Mind test (Difficulty 3) to find the right colors, and three successful tests from anypony will calm the poltergeist right down.

Once its rage has subsided it will apologize for getting so angry. It's just that it can't stand seeing certain colors together; they are such a fashion faux pas. Rainbow Tie will come back into the shop when the screaming and crashing stops. If he looks at the poltergeist's color matches he will declare they are quite debonair and stylish and ask if it can stay and help reorganize some of the rails. The poltergeist will sheepishly agree. If the PCs ask how it arrived, it will say it remembers little except that it arrived in a large house of some form, but it can't say where.

Rainbow Tie

Body: D6	Mind: D6	Charm: D8	Stamina: 12

Talents: Stout Heart (D6), Creative flair - Fashion (D12)

Quirks: *Avant-garde, Highly strung*

Cutie Mark: Bow Tie

Rainbow Tie is an Earth Pony who runs the fashionable clothing boutique 'Canter Klein.' While his clothes are expensive, they are very well made and Rainbow numbers Rarity among his regular customers. However, he doesn't just sell clothes, he offers fashion advice to all his customers and never lets anypony leave his shop looking anything but their best (as far as he is concerned!).

Banshee

The next spirit will be heard before it is seen. A blood curdling scream sounds from a nearby house, and in moments the ponies living there are running for their lives. They will run out of the house utterly terrified as horrible screams echo from the building. Upon seeing the PCs, they will beg for their help. They describe a huge ghostly creature haunting the house, one who screams so loud it actually hurts to hear her.

If the PCs enter the house it will be clear the screams are coming from the upstairs floor. But the problem is getting up there. Each scream is physically painful to hear and strikes the PCs with almost physical force. To force their way up the stairs they must make a Body challenge versus the Banshee's scream of D10. Roll once for the Banshee and see how the PC's rolls match up. Any PCs who rolls less than the Banshee loses stamina equal to the difference between them. If a PC loses 5 points of Stamina from a single test they cannot get up the stairs. The Banshee will keep screaming each round until the PCs can deal with her problem.

If any PCs make it upstairs they will see the Banshee standing on a bed in one of the bedrooms. She is another ghostly apparition in the shape of a huge face with a large mouth. If the PCs look around the room, they will see that there is a mouse sitting in the middle of the bedroom floor. It seems this is what the Banshee is frightened of!

The PCs need to catch the mouse to stop the Banshee screaming. To do this requires a Body test (Difficulty 5) as it is very fast. All the time the Banshee will scream, possibly damaging the PCs further. If they catch the mouse and take it outside, the Banshee will stop screaming and calm down. She will be terribly sorry to scream but she just doesn't like mice at all. She too remembers very little of how she got here, but does remember the house she arrived in had a big red door.

Possession

As the PCs are wandering around the town, a glowing light flies toward them and bounces between them all. They should all make Mind tests, and the PC with the lowest roll is suddenly possessed by a spirit. Their eyes go wide and blank, their movements become robotic and they stop responding to anypony. They only utter one word, 'candy!' and dive toward the nearest source.

The glowing light was another spirit that has now taken over the body of the PC. Unused to having a physical form, they wanted very much to try some candy and they like it. They intend to eat as much as possible, no matter how ill it might make them. Unless the possessed PC is restrained in some way (their Body Trait remains the same) they will try to consume any and all candy in sight. If there is none nearby, they will run off in search of some.

The other PCs might try several things to get rid of the spirit. They might try to talk it out of them, or make the PC unconscious hoping it will leave. But the only way to actually do it is to prove that not all food is tasty. They must make some fake candy out of something really bitter (like broccoli) but nothing so horrible it will poison their friend! Then, if they label their concoction 'candy,' the possessed character will dive right in and eat as much as possible. After a few moments the possessed character will cough and the spirit will fly out of their mouth as fast as it can.

The PC will be left with a horrible taste in their mouth, depending on what they just ate. Interestingly, they were in touch with the spirit's mind while they were possessed and know that the place they are looking for is in the center of town. Putting those clues together – a large house in the center of town with a red door, there is only one place it could be...

The Haunted Mansion

"I'd like to tell ya'll the terrifying tale of the prissy ghost,
who drove everypony crazy with her unnecessary neatness!"
- Applejack

Read Aloud:

Every Nightmare Night, one house in the center of Ponyville becomes a place of mystery and horror. This old mansion becomes haunted for the night, much to the delight of everypony. A rather sullen pony known as 'Dark Shadow' turns his home into a haunted house with the help of some of his friends.

The house is a large old style mansion surrounded by a small fenced garden. Several wooden tombstones have been placed all over the garden, and the old iron fence is covered in cobwebs. Lights flicker inside the house in dark greens and purples, and the occasional scream issues from within. From the gate a thin path snakes between the graves to the large red front door. Nearby, a sign reads 'This way to your worst Nightmare!'

Out of nowhere, an Earth pony appears, his long black mane obscuring his face, his hide the color of night. As screams and laughter echo from the house he whispers to [choose the lead PC] in a dark and mysterious accent.

"Listen to the ponies in the night! What sweet music they make! Welcome to my realm. Enter freely, and leave some of the happiness you bring..."

This pony is Dark Shadow, a rather dramatic pony for whom Nightmare Night is his favorite holiday. While he likes to affect a mysterious and unnerving presence, especially tonight, it doesn't always have the effect on people he'd like. He is here to welcome guests to his haunted house, which he is quite proud of, and rightfully so as it is a popular event. His welcome is designed to help get people in the mood and he will do his best to stay in character.

He will tell the PCs that they enter at their own risk! For the house has been taken over by monsters and creatures from beyond the grave! Each room will be more terrifying than the last, and he cannot promise them that anywhere is safe! To convince him to break character will require a Charm challenge opposed against his Mind (D6). In which case he will tell them anything they want to know about the inside of the house, but be horribly disappointed they will not get the 'full experience.' As far as Dark Shadow knows, everything has gone fine tonight and he hasn't noticed anything strange, at least not for Nightmare Night. Given the amount of pranks and decorations in the town, no pony has noticed the actual spirits leaving the house! Dark Shadow is unlikely to believe there are really ghosts abroad in Ponyville tonight, but he thinks it would be cool if there were.

Anyone is welcome to enter the house. Signs will point out the best way to go but they can wander anywhere they like. Once through the red door, the PCs can go upstairs or down to a basement. The signs (arrows painted in 'blood' – actually tomato sauce) will lead them upstairs, through the various rooms and then down into the basement and back to the front door. Dark Shadow will greet them as they leave, with candy for anypony who tells him what the spookiest part of the house was.

Dark Shadow

Body: D6   **Mind: D6**   **Charm: D6**   **Stamina: 12**

Talents: Stout Heart (D6), Creative flair - Poetry (D8)

Quirks: *Overly Dramatic*

Cutie Mark: Quill

Dark Shadow was originally named 'Candy Flair' until he got his cutie mark and took on a much more dramatic persona. He now dresses only in black and lets his long mane hang over his face all the time. He can be rather tedious to talk to but he organizes a haunted house for Nightmare Night which he enjoys doing immensely even though he'd never admit to getting excited about anything!

Inside the house there are several decorations and dioramas on show that the PCs have to pass through. The game master can create more but some ideas are:

★ A room where all the furniture has been nailed to the ceiling to make it look as if the whole room is upside down.

★ A corridor that is pitch black, but suddenly lights up in ultraviolet ('blacklight') to reveal scary paintings of ghosts and monsters.

★ A room where the walls and furniture are all covered in blood. However, a Mind test (Difficulty 4) and a quick taste will reveal it is tomato sauce. Really good tomato sauce actually and ponies might all like to try some. Dark Shadow won't want to admit it but he will share the recipe with anyone who manages to make a Charm test (Difficulty 6).

★ A bedroom with a false floor that tilts gently as you walk across it, making you feel dizzy. Ponies need to make Body tests (Difficulty 3) to cross it without falling over.

As well as the display rooms, there are a few performers trying to scare the visitors tonight. These ponies are friends of Dark Shadows that he has roped into helping out. None of them quite understand his plan for an artistic and mysteriously unsettling exhibition, but are instead having a whale of a time jumping out at people and scaring them! These characters might be encountered at any time as the PCs wander around the house looking for clues.

Each time one of these characters jumps out at the PCs, they should all make a fear check. Make an opposed roll using Mind against the performer's Charm (D6). Those who fail the challenge get a fear point, but once they gain a fear point they don't get another one on a further failed challenge unless they roll a 1 (but they still get a scare!).

THE PONIES

Noble Bearing the Vampire

This unicorn felt he was the only one with the gravitas to portray a noble vampire count. However, he has gone rather 'cloak happy' flapping it like he is about to fly and used far too much ketchup. He prefers to approach the PC group quite calmly, as if he is a lost foreign pony who needs directions before going vampire crazy.

Storm Chaser the Werewolf

This pegasus was not a fan of wearing a costume that wasn't especially stylish. So instead of trying to look like a wolf he is wearing a very thick and expensive fur coat. His fright style is based on speed as walking is too slow for him. He likes to burst out of a door, power through the PC group and be gone in a moment with a lot of roaring and shouting.

Axel Von Ponyville the Mummy

Axel the earth pony is only joining in reluctantly. He has been wrapped in bandages for hours and they are starting to fall off. This means that the PCs may be forewarned of his fright by seeing a trail of bandages leading to a cupboard, or poking out from a doorway. Axel is only really doing the minimum, walking toward any visitors with arms out and moaning. But he is such a large pony he is still a frightening sight, especially as with the bandages slipping he can't see very well out of them.

Ice Shine and the Ghost

The last member of the haunted house performers is not having a lot of fun. Ice Shine the unicorn was meant to be a ghost. She was wearing a sheet and was rather shy about jumping out at people anyway. But everything started to go wrong when she ran into a real ghost!

As the PCs come into the basement they should make a Mind test (Difficulty 4). Those who succeed see Ice Shine hiding under a table in a sheet. She will beckon them over and explain what is going on. If the PCs don't see Ice Shine, they will walk straight into the spirit. If they think it is a pony dressed up, they need to make a Mind test (Difficulty 2) to realize it isn't. Once they know it is a real spirit they need to make a fear check (Mind test Difficulty 5).

As one of Princess Argent's spirits, this ghost will engage the PCs in a scuffle. If will make itself solid so it can attack them, but it remains a little insubstantial and so reduces any Stamina damage it takes by 2 points. If it is reduced to 0 Stamina, it turns transparent and rushes back through the portal. Anyone who fought it can remove one of their fear points if it is vanquished.

The Portal

In the deepest cellar of the basement is a huge gilded mirror, glowing with a gray light. It casts shadows all about the room which is otherwise littered with old furniture and storage boxes. Anypony who looks in the mirror does not see their reflection. Instead, they see a huge vista of a ruined Ponyville set in a dark sunless land lit by a vast glowing moon. If anypony tries to touch the mirror, their hoof passes straight through! It is clearly some sort of portal to another, scarier version, of Equestria.

Ice Shine will come out of hiding if the ghost has been banished and start looking around the room for something. After a few moments she will gulp and mutter that 'oh dear, they must have thought it was part of the show...'

If the PCs ask her what she means, she will tell them that a group of foals came down here just before the ghost appeared. She thought they were hiding in the room having been trapped. But as she can't find them there is only one place they can have gone: through the mirror...

The Realm of Shadows

"Our world doesn't even make sense!
Why should this one? Who needs continuity?"
- Pinkie Pie

Read Aloud:

From what you can see of the land beyond the mirror, it is a place you really don't want to visit. But there are several foals lost in that place and someone needs to rescue them. Steeling yourself, you step forward into the mirror. It feels like ice cold water against your face as you push through and step into the dark realm on the other side.

Looking around, you seem to have stepped out of a mirror on the ground floor of a ruined building. What remains of the place looks very similar to the house you left in Equestria, as do the rest of the ruins around it. For the most part it looks just like Ponyville, but not a single building remains standing. The moon is full, bathing everything in a mauve and silver glow that is far more chilling than it is magical. There is no sound, but shadows seem to flit from wall to wall. There is a cold breeze blowing through the ruin, which carries moans and sighs around each of you.

Looking around you finally find some tracks, which might be the lost foals. But they lead out of the ruined Ponyville, and toward what appears to be a dark and imposing castle in the distance...

It is quite possible that the PCs will decide this is all too much at this point. So they may try to find the Mane Six or someone else to tell about the portal rather than go through themselves. However, it turns out that the inhabitants of Ponyville have quite a few more problems on their hands. It appears that several more spirits have come through and are now creating havoc all about the town. Ghostly apparitions are floating around scaring people and breaking things all over the place. The Mane Six have a lot on their plate trying to deal with this. So if the PCs ask for advice, any of the Mane six will ask them to go through the portal and find the foals. They are just too busy to help!

However, Twilight Sparkle will be very interested in the portal. She hasn't seen magic like this and it won't take her long to notice some of the hallmarks of the renowned Star Swirl the Bearded. She will want to study the magic in more detail and try to find a way to shut it down. While this means she will be near the portal if the PCs need more advice, she'll be too tied up with her studies to help find the foals.

Entering the Shadow Realm

As soon as the PCs step through the portal, they get a feeling of horror and dread from this dismal place. They should each make a fear check, a Mind test (Difficulty 5), and gain a fear point if they fail. Luckily, given there is nothing specifically scary, they won't feel a need to run away anywhere, although they might be very keen on going back through the portal. However, there are missing foals to be found and the thought of leaving them in this horrible place will be enough to override their fears, for now at least...

While the PCs can recognize this place as Equestria, it is very different. Ponyville lies in ruins; not a single house is standing although there are plenty of remains. It is as if some storm has passed through and destroyed everypony's homes. Luckily, no one seems to be hurt and the whole town is empty. To the south lies the Evertree Forest, just as before. But now it is a dark and ominous place, overgrown with weeds and twisted trees that grow almost conspiratorially close together. The Rambling Rock ridge to the southeast looks sharp and dangerous. Storm clouds full of thunder and lightning cover Cloudsdale to the north. The fields of the Applejack Farm are ruined and desolate. In the distance, where Canterlot should be, is a very different castle. While it is mostly the same size and shape as Canterlot its towers are thin and twisted, its stone black and full of shadows. The trail left by the foals leads in this direction, and it is the only place nearby that looks as if it might be inhabited.

The PCs might want to take a look around Ponyville before setting off. It is quite upsetting as while this isn't their Ponyville, it looks very much the same. Seeing it laid waste like this is bound to make them wonder about their own homes. What they don't know is that this devastation was intentional. After the defeat of Princess Solar, the residents of Ponyville tried to stand up to Princess Argent. For their temerity she destroyed the entire town, scattering those who survived across the country to find sanctuary elsewhere.

Wandering the ruined Ponyville is actually quite scary. The light flickers against the remains of the buildings and the ruins could still hide all manner of monsters and shadows. As they walk between the fallen walls and broken homes, it will seem as if something is moving in the corner of their eye all the time. Each PC should be allowed a Mind test (Difficulty 5), and if they succeed, they catch a glimpse of something actually watching them. There are several shadow creatures lurking here as spies for Princess Argent. They are almost indistinguishable from shadows and utterly loyal to their Queen. Several are already flitting toward the castle to inform her of the PC's arrival. Should any of the PCs attempt to scuffle with one of them they will just run away, moving like liquid through the shadows.

Additionally, if only to unnerve the PCs, those who wander Ponyville will find the broken remains of something that was important to them in their world. The game master should allow them to find such things as they move around the town, underlining the horror of what has happened here, and perhaps foreshadowing the fate of their own Ponyville if this menace cannot be stopped. Some suggestions are:

★ A favorite toy, broken and burned

★ Their own home with a door they painted only this morning torn and flaked by heat

★ A picture of the character and some friends torn and half burned

★ A favorite spot, such as a garden or park that is now ruined

Traveling the Shadow Realm

It is a bit of a walk to the dark castle that appears to be a twisted version of Canterlot, and one that feels all the longer for trekking through the Shadow Realm. In this place it is always night, the only light issuing from the silver moon that burns in the bleak sky. The whole place gives its visitors a looming feeling of dread, made all the worse by offering no clear source of the evil. The whole place just feels wrong, and it is a hard feeling to shake.

It will take the PCs a couple of hours to reach the castle (or rather the next encounter). So to liven up the journey and emphasize the strange presence of the place, the game master may want to throw a couple of random encounters at the players. Two or three should be all you need, but it really depends on how long you want the journey to be. Simply roll a D20 and apply the result, or pick what you think sounds fun. The game master should also feel free to expand and adjust any of these encounters as they like, or even create more of their own. But if you do, remember they should just be simple encounters at this point.

Roll	The Shadow Realm Random Event Table
1-2	Something about this place makes all the PCs feel drained and tired. They must each make a Body test (Difficulty 4). If they fail, they lose 1 stamina for each point they failed by. If they succeed they still lose 1 Stamina.
3-4	Scattered on the ground near the trail are a pile of small stones that all glow with a mysterious silver light. They are actually perfectly safe (but the PCs won't know that...) and can absorb moonlight. They remain glowing with light (about a candle's worth) for 3 hours after being taken out of the moonshine.
5-6	In the darkness, the PCs fail to see a crevice in the road. They must all make a Mind test (Difficulty 4) to notice it or trip over and lose 2 stamina.
7-8	The group steps into an area that is completely pitch black. Each should make a Mind test (Difficulty 5) or get lost. Anyone who gets lost finds themselves coming out of the area on their own. The group will have to track each other down, although lone characters might run into the Hooves of Light and be rescued.
9-10	A ghostly spirit flies up to the PCs and warns them to "Beware!" If they are not frightened by it, Mind test (Difficulty 4), they can ask it what they should beware of. The spirit will be surprised they ask as most people run away. It will tell them that the castle they are traveling toward is the lair of Princess Argent, the Queen of Fear, and that they had better turn around.
11-12	The PCs come across an item that belongs to one of the foals they are looking for, proving they are on the right track. It might be a toy, some Nightmare Night candy or perhaps a cloak or piece of costume.
13-14	As they travel, one of the PCs steps on the lair of a giant trapdoor spider. The spider lives in a small burrow and leaps out to grab anything that passes by. It will try to drag the PC into its lair, requiring a Body test to resist (Difficulty 5). If the PC can't make the test, other PCs can try to help pull them free.
15-16	A strange black cloud appears to be approaching the PCs, but if they move to avoid it, the cloud follows them. It is actually a cloud of living shadow, a spy for Princess Argent. The PCs must make a Body test (Difficulty 6) to escape it. Those who fail the test are engulfed by the cloud of flying screaming shadows who do their best to terrify them. Anyone caught in the cloud should make a Fear Test (Difficulty 6). Physical attacks cannot damage the shadows, but they will leave if anyone uses a magical attack on them. After frightening at least one PC they will leave to cause mayhem elsewhere.
17-18	The PCs come across a pool of black inky water. If they fail a Mind test (Difficulty 5), they cannot resist feeling horribly thirsty and drinking from the pool. If they do, they receive a vision of their worst nightmare and gain a fear point. The player might want to describe what their character experienced.
19	The sky grows dark and Princess Argent attacks the PCs! She flies out of the sky and engages in a scuffle with them to see how dangerous they are. She will fight for two rounds before flying or teleporting away with an evil laugh.
20	Roll twice on this table. Both events occur!

The Hooves of Light

*"I saw the signs of Nightmare Moon's return,
and I knew it was you who had the magic inside to defeat her."*
- Princess Celestia

As the PCs wander the Shadow Realm, they are being watched, but not only by the forces of Princess Argent. The forces of good are battered and defeated, but still fighting. They have taken notice of the arrival of the foals and the PCs, but don't quite know if they can be trusted. They have suffered plenty of times from traps set by the forces of shadow. However, they have decided they need to know more about the PCs, as it is possible they could be allies.

These forces of good are led by Princess Solar, Argent's sister, and this realm's version of Celestia. When Princess Solar was defeated by her sister she was expelled from the land and her light with her. It took her many years to recover, and she is still not strong enough to face her sister again, especially since Argent has only grown in power. So instead, Solar reached out to what friends she could find and began to build an organization to usurp Princess Argent. This group calls itself the 'Hooves of Light,' and while its membership is quite small, they are extremely loyal to their goals. All of them are dedicated to reclaiming the Equestria they love from the shadow of Princess Argent and her minions.

The following encounter should take place as the PCs journey toward the castle, but it might also be used to pull them back on the right track if they choose to investigate somewhere else. The game master might space the events out with events from the Shadow Realm Random Events table.

Watchers in the Shadow

As soon as the PCs come through the mirror, the Hooves of Light will notice them. They will assign some of their number to track and watch the PCs, and listen to their conversations, to figure out if they can be trusted. However, it will take them a long time to decide the PCs are not just part of a very clever deception to root out the remaining dissidents to Princess Argent's rule. They will keep their distance until the PCs leave Ponyville. The game master might allow the PCs a Mind test (Difficulty 5) to notice they are being watched. However, they may dismiss it as part of the general feelings of paranoia the realm inspires. If anyone manages an amazing success (rolls a 10 or higher) they will catch a glimpse of something pony shaped in the distance, but it will be gone before they can investigate any further. The Hooves are very careful and have learned not to get too close to anything potentially dangerous.

Ambush!

After the Hooves have seen the PCs deal with at least one encounter, they may consider making contact. If they show real friendship looking after each other, or it is clear the minions of shadow have it in for them as well, the Hooves will decide to get a little closer. But they won't just walk up and say hello. Just in case the PCs are dangerous, they will want to make sure they are in charge of the situation at all times.

So the Hooves will make their first encounter with the PCs an ambush! Dressed in their dark armor, a group of three pegasi carrying a net will sweep out from hiding and drop the net on as many of the PCs as they can. Each PC will have to make a Body test at Difficulty 6 to avoid the net.

As soon as the net is dropped, another five earth pony Hooves of Light soldiers will come out of hiding and point spears at the PCs. A unicorn soldier will then step forward and demand the PCs surrender. The unicorn is Commander Daring, who is in charge of the squad.

PCs are not usually very good at surrendering, so this may mean everything goes a bit crazy! Those caught in the net will be mostly powerless as they are tangled up in it. However, they can use any magical abilities. Anypony who escaped the net is free to do as they please, but there are Hooves of Light pegasi to catch up with any flyers. The soldiers on the ground can deal with anyone else. Commander Daring's anti-magic power might stop any unicorns teleporting away.

What the PCs don't know is that they are still being tested. The soldiers will not attack unless the PCs engage them in a scuffle. Anyone who runs away will be allowed to leave. What Commander Daring wants to know is how violent or dangerous the PCs are before taking them to Princess Solar. If they surrender, they will be treated well but taken captive. Those who run are the sort of ponies who desert their friends as far as Daring is concerned. Anyone who fights might be respected for not giving in, but considered a fool for fighting against such a superior force and wasting energy they might later use to escape.

The look of the soldiers may well make the PCs think they work for Princess Argent. So anything they say about how they won't surrender to evil will actually help convince the commander they can be trusted.

Whatever the PCs do, there are two outcomes for them. They either escape or are forced to surrender. If they get out of the net and leave their friends, the soldiers let them go. Anyone who fights will have to scuffle with all the soldiers. If they are knocked out (which is likely) they will be left where they fall. However, if they have proved brave and honest they may be picked up and taken with the others. Anyone else will be taken prisoner, and the soldiers will take them to their hideout. PCs who escaped so they could rescue their friends will have to track the soldiers. However, their trail doesn't lead to the dark castle, but out toward a nearby twisted forest.

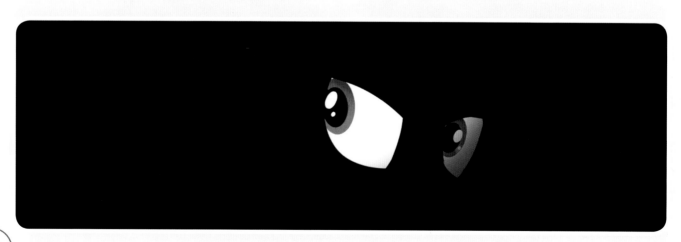

Commander Daring

Body: D10   **Mind: D8**   **Charm: D6**   **Stamina: 18**

Talents: Stout Heart (D10), Magic resistance (D10)

Quirks: *Serious, Optimistic*

Special: Commander Daring can create a zone where magic is harder to perform. When she creates this zone, the Commander rolls her magic resistance (D10) and that number is eplaces the Difficulty of all magic tests in the area if it is higher than the original difficulty. The effect lasts for as long as the Commander concentrates, but she cannot use any other magic while it is running.

Cutie Mark: a broken wand

The unit commander is one of Princess Solar's most trusted lieutenants. Daring has proved herself in several conflicts but always makes the safety of her unit as her priority.

Commander Daring wears metal barding which reduces stamina loss by 2 whenever losing stamina from a physical source (see Core Rulebook p81).

Soldiers of the Hooves of Light

Body: D8   **Mind: D6**   **Charm: D4**   **Stamina: 14**

Talents: Stout Heart (D10), The Stare (D6)

Quirks: *Serious, Dedicated*

The members of the Hooves of Light appear quite intimidating. Not only are they rather serious, but they all wear full barding armor made of a black metal to allow them to sneak around the Shadow Realm more easily. While most of the soldiers are Earth Ponies, there are several Pegasi and Unicorns among their ranks.

The soldiers wear metal barding which reduces stamina loss by 2 whenever losing stamina from a physical source (see Core Rulebook p81).

The Hideout of the Hooves

The captured PCs will be taken into a deep, dark wood nearby. The soldiers will answer none of their questions, only telling them to behave and be quiet. Commander Daring will tell any of the PCs who have earned her respect that they do not work for Princess Argent, but she won't say any more than that.

After a long walk (where the PCs may just be dragged in the net) the group will be taken through what appears to be impenetrable forest that suddenly opens up into a clearing surrounded by treehouses. This is the Hooves' main hideout, a woodland camp protected by an illusion of forest maintained by Solar's magic.

The camp is made up of several camouflaged huts and tree houses nestled between the trees. Several more soldiers stand guard, but there are also ordinary ponies and foals living here in hiding. The PCs will be brought before Princess Solar, who will stare at them thoughtfully. Her horn then glows with light and she relaxes a little.

"I can detect goodness in these ponies," she tells her followers. "But we still have to be sure."

There is a murmured ascent from the assembled Hooves of Light.

Princess Solar looks to the PCs again and asks each one of them to come forward and explain how they have fought for the side of good in their lives. This is an opportunity for each of the PCs to tell a story of their proudest moment from their adventures. If this is their first adventure, each may have already played a part in helping the lost spirits. But even if they haven't, the fact they have come into the Shadow Realm to find some lost foals is more than enough.

Princess Solar

Body: D10   **Mind: D20**   **Charm: D20**   **Stamina: 30**

Talents: Telekinesis (D10), Fly (D10), Stout Heart (D20), Creative Flair: Leadership (D20), Stun Ray (D12), Teleport (D10), Force field (D20)

Quirks: *Dedicated*

Cutie Mark: Sun

Solar looks just like Princess Celestia, but at the same time is very different. She carries a few scars from her battles with her sister and she seems downcast and a little defeated. However, she remains defiant and despite the lack of the usual glamour and regality of Celestia, Solar is every inch the leader of her people.

Each PC should make a Charm test, with a Difficulty between 2-5 depending on how good the game master thinks their story is. Those who succeed will prove to Princess Solar they are worth trusting. While she won't consider those who fail to be clearly working for Princess Argent, she will not entirely trust them quite yet.

If any more PCs turn up (having followed the group) they will be expected to tell a story too. The fact they have come to help their friends proves them worth the benefit of any doubt. However, they may have trouble finding the camp as unless they follow very closely, they won't be able to see through the camouflage illusion that protects the hideout. If they have a trail to lead them to it, it is still a Mind test (Difficulty 8) to see it is an illusion. If they can't see where to go, just going into the forest will get them lost. Their only other option will be to wait for their friends to come out.

After they have shared stories, the Hooves of Light will offer the PCs something to eat and a place to rest. If any of them have lost any Stamina, they can refresh their points back to full again. Princess Solar will heal them with magic, even though it clearly weakens and tires her.

If they haven't already explained their story, the PCs can tell Princess Solar what they are doing here, and ask her about what is going on in this realm. She will explain their history and how her sister defeated her. But she will be very interested to hear about 'Nightmare Moon.' If seems Princess Argent hasn't managed to make the transition from Princess to Nightmare Moon, the way Princess Luna did. Solar will warn the PCs that if Argent finds out about Nightmare Moon she will want to invade Equestria to claim such secrets of power and dark magic for herself!

If the PCs know about the Helm of Shadows, and tell Princess Solar about it, she will be very concerned. She will tell them that she has long suspected that Princess Argent is researching dark magic that will enhance her power even further. She wants to become another version of Nightmare Moon herself. If she should learn of a magical item in the PC's world that will solve her problem, she will spare no effort to claim it. Even if the PCs know nothing about the Helm, Princess Solar will realize that for Princess Luna to become Nightmare Moon, she must have created something like the Helm of Shadows. Even the suspicion that such an item may exist in the PC's Equestria will be enough for Princess Argent to launch a full scale invasion. What began as a journey to rescue lost foals may well have to become a fight to stop a terrible evil trying to invade and conquer Equestria!

If the PCs ask about the foals, Princess Solar will hang her head with shame. She tells the PCs that the Hooves have seen some foals (about six of them) wandering toward the castle in strange costumes. They thought it was some sort of trap and so avoided them. But the realization that these were just lost foals in need of help greatly upsets Princess Solar. She cannot spare much, but she will do all she can to rescue the foals who are now undoubtedly prisoners of Princess Argent.

There is a useful secret Princess Solar will share with the PCs to help them get into the castle. She can give them the location of a small sewer tunnel outlet where the gateway has rusted and broken. It will lead directly into the castle and is unlikely to be guarded. The Hooves have been saving this information as their trump card for the day they can take the castle. But Princess Solar is willing to risk its discovery to help the foals.

If there is anything else the PCs require, Princess Solar will do her best to provide it. She can spare two sets of armor and some spears if that will help. But she will warn that if they try to fight Princess Argent directly, they have as good as lost already. One of her soldiers will guide the PCs to the tunnel entrance (unless they are set on trying to go into the castle by the front door!) and another patrol will set out to collect any other PCs still outside the hideout and bring them to the tunnel entrance.

The Castle Of Fear

"Do you think there's a single room in this castle that isn't filled with terrifying things?"
- Applejack

Read Aloud:

Where the beautiful castle of Canterlot stands in your world, there is now a brooding fortress of nightmares. While Princess Argent's castle appears to have been built to much the same design, the two castles could not be more different. Before you stands a building made of night black stone. Each turret seems to claw at the sky instead of reaching toward it gracefully and each window seems to be glaring back at you with hatred. Moans echo all around the place, and spirits can be seen flitting between the twisted towers.

But the foals you need to rescue are in there somewhere. From what you can see there is only one way in: through the great main gate that is guarded by two soldiers. That is, unless you have found a more secret path...

Getting Inside

There are two ways to get into the Castle of Fear: either through the front door or (if the PCs have met and impressed Princess Solar) through the secret tunnel entrance.

Getting through the front door is difficult, but not impossible. If the PCs pretend to be spies returning from a mission, looking to report to Princess Argent, they will be allowed to enter. They will just have to make a Charm test (Difficulty 4) to be convincing with their story. Generally, the guards figure that no one with any sense would willingly walk into the castle so they are not too picky. However, if the PCs are not convincing the guards will attempt to arrest them, and call for backup (which will arrive swiftly in the form of at least two more guards for each PC!).

If the guards allow the PC's inside, they will be directed toward the throne room. A small dragon much like Spike called Talon will be summoned to direct them there. If the PCs slip away from Talon, he will raise the alarm and warn Princess Argent there are intruders. This will mean guards will be wandering all around the castle looking for the PCs.

The other way to get inside the castle is through the old drainage entrance Princess Solar has revealed to them. They can access the tunnels from a grating hidden in the forest within sight of the castle. The grating is old and broken so they can easily climb down into the tunnels through there. The tunnels are quite low and built of brick and stone. As they have been designed as drains there is a knee high layer of rather nasty looking water running through them. The water isn't dangerous, but it is a bit smelly and we'd recommend no one drinks it!

The path to the castle is a simple one: just follow the tunnel. If a PC wants to stay out of the water they can make a test of their choice; each is Difficulty 4. A Body test allows them to climb around the walls, a Mind test lets them see a path that lets them keep away from the water, and a Charm test might convince another PC to carry them! Other than being unpleasant, the water has no other effect and after a long walk through the dark the PCs will come upon a large iron gate that leads into the dungeons.

Castle Guards

Body: D8	Mind: D6	Charm: D4	Stamina: 14

Talents: Stout Heart (D10)

Quirks: *Humorless*

The soldiers guarding the castle are those ponies who pledged their allegiance to Princess Argent. Most of them are bullies or just too frightened to say no to her. It is possible that the PCs might make friends with some and convince them to join Princess Solar. But they should be careful about revealing too much of what they know about her hideout!

The guards are clad in grand silver armor. Each is armed with a nasty looking halberd. Most are Earth Ponies, but there is also an elite flying unit of Pegasi. There are few, if any, Unicorns as Princess Argent refuses to allow anyone but her to practice magic.

The castle guards all *wear metal barding which reduces stamina loss by 2 whenever losing stamina from a physical source (see Core Rulebook p81).* This armor includes a full helm and will make an excellent disguise if the PCs can steal or find some.

Wandering the Castle

There are two main areas of the castle the PCs will want to get to. The dungeons are where most of the foals are being kept, and the Throne Room is where Princess Argent is frightening two of them. However, there is plenty of the castle to explore and the game master is free to create any manner of rooms and places they might come across.

In general, the whole place is dark and forbidding. The walls are cold black stone and the only decorations are flags with the emblem of Princess Argent on them. Guards do patrol the corridors and the PCs may have to sneak into a room to hide as some pass by. If they end up having a scuffle with any of the guards and don't manage to knock them out, the guards will raise the alarm. If this happens, there will be guards everywhere and all attempts to sneak about will be twice as hard.

Places to Explore

The game master may want to restrict the adventure to just the dungeons and throne room. But they may want the PCs to explore a little further. There is a lot of fun to be had dodging guards around the castle looking for the right rooms. There may be plenty of treasures for the PCs to pick up too if they want to risk it. So the GM is encouraged to create new rooms, use the stat blocks opposite, and expand on the detail we offer here. To get you started, here are a few examples:

Guardroom: The PCs walk into a room full of guards! They might be asleep, so the PCs have to tip toe around to avoid waking them. But they might be awake and leap to attack, chasing the PCs all over the place. The room contains many uniforms, armor, and weapons.

Laboratory: This large room is where Princess Argent does her magical experiments. It is a smelly and unpleasant place, but still full of many useful magical tools, ingredients and potions. There may also be magical creatures that will be very glad of rescue, or maybe a few potions or mysterious enchanted items that might be useful too.

Bedrooms: Everyone needs to sleep somewhere and many of the rooms will be bedrooms. Some are small guest rooms, while others are large plush boudoirs for the nobility, or even Princess Argent herself. There might be any manner of personal possessions and clothes in these rooms, depending on the occupant.

Library: Books are great and this room is full of them. There will be plenty of places to hide behind shelves if the PCs are being chased. It will also have several rare and important texts, mostly on magic. Many might have some interesting tricks and techniques undiscovered in Equestria.

Spider Swarm

Body: -   **Mind:** D4   **Charm:** D4   **Stamina:** 14

Talents: Spider-climb (D8), Swarm (D10)

Quirks: *Animal*

The dozens of tiny spiders swarming together use their Swarm (D10) instead of a Body score. In the Castle of Fear, spiders have learned to move together in curious, almost fluid swarming formations.

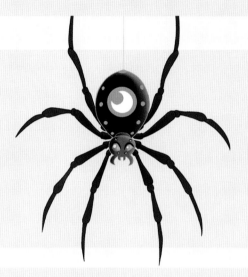

Night-terror Spider

Body: D10   **Mind:** D8   **Charm:** D4   **Stamina:** 18

Talents: Spider-climb (D8), Web Sling (D6), Tremor Sense: Webs (D6)

Quirks: *Fear: Sunlight, Fear: Fire*

For the Hooves of Light, these 'Night-terrors' have become something of a symbol of the Queen's tyranny.

Bat Swarm

Body: -   **Mind:** D6   **Charm:** D4   **Stamina:** 14

Talents: Fly (D6), Swarm (D8)

Quirks: *Animal*

Though cute, a swarm of bats can be seriously scary. Moving as a swarm, the bats have a habit of appearing from behind doors just opened, flying through narrow tunnels, and wheeling creepily in the air above anypony who comes near the castle. The swarm of bats uses use their Swarm (D10) instead of a Body score.

Giant Bat

Body: D10   **Mind:** D6   **Charm:** D4   **Stamina:** 16

Talents: Fly (D10), Shove (D6)

Quirks: *Animal*

Giant Bats circle in sinister spirals around the towers of the Castle of Fear, letting loose horrible cries and screeches that echo eerily across the land below. They will often ignore approaching ponies unless provoked.

The Dungeons

Down in the bottom of the castle are the dungeons. This area is quite large with an open plan, with a row of cells along each wall. There are about 30 cells in total (15 on each side) which are built out of iron bars to allow the guards to watch what the prisoners are up to. Having defeated most of her enemies, the Queen's dungeons are almost empty apart from four frightened foals. They are huddled together in pairs in two of the cells.

In the middle of the room is a small table where four guards are keeping watch. They are not expecting any trouble and so are in the middle of a card game. None of them is keeping an eye on the entrance. This means the PCs will have the element of surprise, but it is up to them whether they try to beat the guards in the scuffle or deceive them in some way.

If the PCs make a sneak attack, the guards will be unable to roll anything but a D4 to defend themselves for the first round. So there is a chance they could be knocked out easily on a good roll. Once the first round is over, the scuffle continues as normal. Luckily, there are no more guards around here as dungeon guarding is a pretty boring job and none of the others want to do it. So the alarm will only be raised if all the PCs are knocked out and the guards can find someone to tell!

If the PCs try to talk their way in, it is up to the game master how clever or convincing their story is. One option is to tell the guards they have orders to take the foals for questioning or to Princess Argent. Given that Argent is interrogating pairs of foals in turns this is not too strange a request. If the PCs have thought to get hold of a guard's uniform, any attempts to convince the guards of a deception will be much easier.

If the PCs can find a way to free the foals (and haven't already been to the throne room) the foals will tell them what is going on. They thought this was all part of the haunted house, and quickly learned their mistake, but sadly not quickly enough to avoid getting captured. Princess Argent has had her guards bring them in pairs to the throne room. There she scares them for a while and appears to draw power from their fear before having them taken back to the dungeon and swapped for another pair. So there will still be two foals missing, but they may be coming back soon, with guards!

The PCs should decide quickly if they are going to lie in wait for the guards to return the other foals, try to ambush them in the corridors or even rescue them from the throne room. The foals will tell them that usually there are two guards to bring them to the throne room each time.

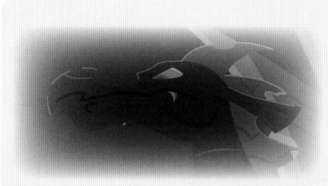

Gargoyle

Body: D12   **Mind: D6**   **Charm: D4**   **Stamina: 18**

Talents: The Stare! (D8), Fly (D4)

Quirks: *Unliving*

Special: On an amazing success, The Stare talent is not used to control ponies but instead will turn them to stone! A gargoyle may choose to release a creature turned to stone whenever it wishes.

Lost Foals

The six lost foals have the same statistics as the foals the PCs were looking after for Nightmare Night. The game master is free to create characters for all of them in the same way. But if you don't have time, here is a quick guide to them and the Nightmare Night costumes they are wearing that you can expand or adjust as you like.

Sea Spray: Earth Pony who loves swimming, Witch costume

Dust Dash: Earth Pony who likes to run around, Vampire costume

Sparkle Motion: Unicorn who lives to study, Ghost costume

Treacle Bake: Unicorn who loves eating pie, Chef costume

Echo Force: Pegasus who is always really loud, Ringmaster costume

Downdraft: Pegasus who sulks a lot, Devil costume

The Throne Room

The throne room is the easiest room to find in the castle, as pretty much every corridor leads to it eventually. However, the PCs would do well to avoid it, as this is where Princess Argent can usually be found. However, she will be intimidating some foals that they need to rescue depending on the PC's plan. The cries from the foals, and the laughter of Princess Argent will be clearly heard the closer the PCs get to the throne room.

The room itself is much like the one in Canterlot, but with none of its joy, kindness, and beauty. The throne here is designed not to impress visitors with grandeur and make them feel as if everything is being run efficiently, but to make them feel small and powerless against the might of the Queen of Fear. The place is decorated with Princess Argent's flag, and contains a large balcony where she can look out over her domain.

If the PCs haven't rescued all the foals, there will be two in here, shivering as Princess Argent looms above them, full of rage and flame. Princess Argent is an impressive figure. It should be clear that the PCs shouldn't try to take her on alone! The mere sight of her trying to intimidate the foals is worth a fear (Mind) test at Difficulty 6. The best plan is to let her finish with the foals (which she will do very soon) and grab them from the guards as they are taken back to their cell.

However, it will be hard to stand by and wait while Princess Argent scares them so much. The game master might allow a Mind test (Difficulty 3) for a PC to realize what they are up against and not dive in recklessly. But on the other hand, it is possible to rescue the foals without directly confronting Princess Argent. If some of the PCs create a distraction, some other PCs might be able to sneak in and grab the foals. They are too upset to offer any resistance at this point.

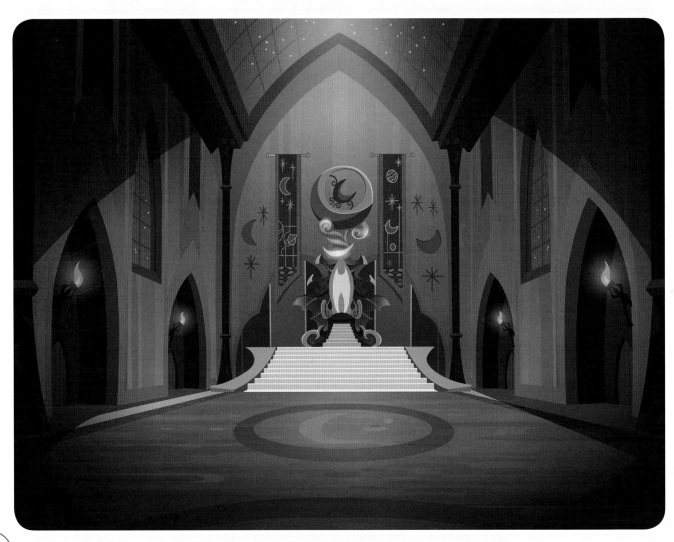

Princess Argent, The Queen of Fear

Body: D20 **Mind: D20** **Charm: D20** **Stamina: 40**

Talents: Princess (D12), Telekinesis (D20), Fly (D20), Stout Heart (D20), Creative Flair: Scaring (D20), Stun Ray (D12), Teleport (D10), Invisibility (D12), Force field (D20)

Quirks: *Frightening, Power hungry*

Argent looks just like Princess Luna, but as frightening and terrible as Nightmare Moon. She desperately seeks a way to 'ascend' and become a new version of Nightmare Moon. She will stop at nothing to claim any new power or dark magic that might help her do this. In her studies she has unlocked the power of fear and can draw energy from the terror of those around her. She may reroll any die once by spending a fear point.

Escaping the Castle

Once the PCs have the foals, they have no reason to stick around. Their best plan is to return to the portal and get back to Equestria. Princess Argent is far too powerful for them to take on, although maybe one day they might be able to return and help Princess Solar and the Hooves of Light.

How they leave will be determined by how subtle they were in the castle. If they have been quiet and remained undetected, they can leave the castle quietly. But if the alarm is raised, Princess Argent and her guards will chase the PCs out of the castle! In this case it will be a race to get to the portal! While the player characters will have a head start, the foals will be slow. The game master should let them escape, but not make it easy for them! They should ramp up the tension describing the army of soldiers and spirits giving chase. Even if the PCs have been subtle, it won't be long before Princess Argent finds the foals are missing and orders her army to find them.

When the PCs reach the portal they can run straight through. But Princess Argent and her army are right behind them. Thankfully Princess Argent orders the army to stop before any of them enter the portal. She steps forward and uses her magic to test the portal for traps. She taps at it and pulls back as sparks shower around her. It appears that Star Swirl the Bearded's magical protections on the mirror have remained intact. Princess Argent is too dreadful to enter Equestria, for now...

Shadow Busters

Read Aloud:

Breathing a sigh of relief you all tumble back through the portal, leaving the Shadow Realm behind. Much to your surprise, Twilight Sparkle herself is standing before you, her horn glowing brightly with magic. But after only a moment, she slumps her shoulders in defeat.

"It's no good," she says. "The portal just won't close. Something is holding it open."

"Is it something from this Shadow Realm?" asks Rarity coming up beside her.

"No, I think whatever is keeping it open is in Equestria. But I've no idea what that might be."

As you look at the portal, you notice in terror that Princess Argent stands before the portal at the head of a large army. She is poised to invade Equestria! Her horn blazes with dark energy, and black fire streaks toward you. But it fails to pass through, and Princess Argent's screams of rage echo even in Equestria. It seems she can't pass through, but it doesn't look like she is ready to give up!

With a chilling smile, Princess Argent spreads her wings and calls out to the dark clouds that are gathering behind her. With a crash of lightning, four monstrous shapes form out of the clouds and power toward the portal. While Twilight Sparkle does her best to try and close the gateway these huge spectral shadows force their way through into Equestria, tearing apart the haunted house as they explode into Ponyville, to the laughter of Princess Argent.

Thanks to the ancient magic of Star Swirl the Bearded, Princess Argent and her soldiers are unable to enter the portal. It was enchanted to only allow creatures attuned to the Elements of Harmony to pass through, although the insubstantial nature of the spirits allows them to circumvent these safeguards. But under an assault by Princess Argent, those protections won't last for long! In the meantime, Princess Argent summons huge Mega Shadow creatures to cause chaos and stop the Mane Six or the PCs closing the portal before she can break through.

The Mega Shadows are essentially huge spirits formed from magic. They can change their form to any dimension they like, allowing them to be thin enough to pass through the mirror and huge enough to flatten buildings. As they power through the portal they punch massive holes in the haunted house and sweep off into the night. As screams and shouts echo around Ponyville, the thump of Princess Argent's dark magic continues to hammer at the other side of the mirror.

Who you gonna call?

Things may look dire with a proto-Nightmare Moon about to break into Equestria and monstrous spirits smashing up the town. But all is not lost by a long shot. Twilight Sparkle has a plan. Some time ago she came across some magical crystals that can channel and store magical power and the elements of harmony. She built them into a collection of gadgets that might be just what is needed to deal with the Mega Shadows. She will tell the PCs to go to her house and get Spike to find the devices while she holds off Princess Argent.

At Twilight's house, Spike will know what the PCs are after, but warn them the devices are completely untested and potentially dangerous. But it's not as if there is any other option! There are two types of device. The first is a simple crystal cut in the shape of a closed flower. The other is a backpack with some sort of hose/blaster attached to it. There will be enough of these devices to equip each PC with a pack and give the group one crystal for each of the four Mega Shadows.

Spike will explain that the backpack can collect the energy from the Elements of Harmony, then use the hose to blast that power at a target. He thinks this should weaken the Mega Shadows enough for them to use the crystals to trap and store them. The crystals will have to be placed near the weakened Mega Shadow, where they will open and draw them inside. While these crystals will keep the Mega Shadows contained, there will only be room for one in each trap. Spike will wish the PCs luck and say he would join them, but there is a very real chance all the devices will explode and so he'd rather not! Luckily he thinks an explosion is only likely if the packs are operated at full strength for very long, but that is all he knows.

Harmony against Shadow

Armed with the packs and trap crystals, the PCs can set off to try and take on the Mega Shadows. They won't have to search for long, and almost immediately they will find one chasing a group of ponies around the town. To defeat the creature the PCs have to use the packs to reduce its Stamina, then they can try to contain it with the trap crystal.

To use the packs, the PC has to conjure up their own Element of Harmony and focus it into the device. To do this the player should tell the rest of the group about an experience their character has had that inspired their Element of Harmony, as their character is focusing on the experience. This experience might be one of their previous adventures, or something the player invents to add to their character's backstory. The following list might help you remember or think of a story:

Laughter
This might be a joke they found especially funny or an experience they had with a friend that made them both laugh.

Honesty
This might be a time they told the truth even when it meant admitting something they'd rather not disclose.

Kindness
This might be a time they took a moment to see to someone else's needs instead of their own.

Generosity
This might be when they gave something away that they'd rather have kept, and how the person they gave it to did something great with it.

Loyalty
This might be when the character stood by either a person or a principle when they could have just ignored the problem.

Magic
This might be when a particular spell finally worked for the first time, or when they discovered a new piece of magical knowledge.

Once the PC has focused on an experience, the pack glows and sparks, and then suddenly an energy beam fires out of the hose like liquid magic. The first blast will cause the Mega Shadow it is pointed it at to lose D6 Stamina. If on the next round if the PC can think of a different story to focus more of their Element of Harmony, they can improve this to a D8.

Each new story improves the damage die by 1 step up to a maximum of D20. However, if the damage die rolls a 20, it explodes, doing 20 Stamina damage to both the target and the PC. Any pack charged up to a D20 will begin to spark and bellow out smoke as a warning it is overheating! As the packs become empowered with the Elements of Harmony, the PCs may choose to split up to take on more than one Mega Shadow at a time. The game master should emphasize how they are smashing up houses and terrifying the inhabitants of Ponyville, making time a factor.

There are four Mega Shadows, that each have 30 Stamina points. However, they are not going to come quietly. Each time they are blasted with energy they will attack the PCs. They are so large they can attack everyone who attacked them that round. They expand with a rush of energy and dark magic, trying to buffet and engulf their opponents. Each character that is attacked needs to make a Body test at Difficulty 4 to dodge the worst of the attack. If they succeed, they still lose 1 Stamina point. If they fail, they lose 3 Stamina points, and if they roll a one they lose 6 Stamina points!

When a Mega Shadow is reduced to 0 Stamina, it will appear woozy and stop attacking. At this point the crystal can be thrown under it to try and trap it. The crystal flower will open automatically when it is in the right position, but it will take a Body test (Difficulty 3) to throw it in the right place. If the test fails the Mega Shadow will recover a little and regain 10 Stamina points, resuming the fight! If the test is a success, a golden light bursts from the crystal and envelops the Mega Shadow. Then, in a moment the light and the Mega Shadow are pulled into the crystal with a snap. The crystal turns black and gentle, smokes but is otherwise safe unless someone is foolish enough to try and break it!

As the PCs charge up their packs they might split up to take on more than one Mega Shadow at the same time. If they discover what it takes to make a pack explode they might choose to reduce the power, which they can do at any time by 1 dice step. If they lose any packs there are no more replacements so they have better be careful!

The Library

Once they have defeated one of the Mega Shadows, each time they trap another one the PCs can make a Mind test at Difficulty 5 (-1 for each trapped Mega Shadow). If they succeed, they notice the Mega Shadows are actually trying to protect rather than destroy a particular building in Ponyville. They are doing their best to make sure no pony can get to the place either. While there is a single Mega Shadow around, there is no way to reach the library, but once they are all gone the PCs may well want to investigate.

The library is quite a large building, but with the celebrations, and now the invasion going on, no one was thought to be inside. However, shivering in a corner under a desk, surrounded by books about Nightmare Moon, is Summer. This foal is the reason the portal was awoken and her fear is the reason it can't be shut. She had decided to prove she wasn't scared by reading about Nightmare Moon, but that didn't work. Then she thought she'd keep reading, as surely one of the books would show how she could be defeated and she'd be less scared. That didn't work either; instead it just made her more afraid. Her fear, and the fact it was Nightmare Night, caused the portal to open.

Princess Argent used her magic to uncover the truth about the portal, and has been sending her horrible visions of what she plans to do to both her and Equestria when she invades.

Now all Summer can do is cower under one of the tables and hope the spirits, shadows, and visions stop.

If the PCs look around the library they will have to make a Mind test (Difficulty 3) to even find Summer. Then it will take a Charm test at (Difficulty 5) to get her to come out from under the table!

Any Unicorn (or pony whose Element of Harmony is Magic) will be able to see the magical connection between Summer and the portal on a Mind test (Difficulty 4). If they fail to notice it, Twilight Sparkle certainly won't.

The problem is that Summer doesn't look like she is in much shape to stop being afraid. But to close the portal she needs to lay her fears to rest, and she can only do that by facing Princess Argent herself. It is going to be pretty difficult to convince her given how hard it is just to get her to come out from under the table!

Facing Fear

Equestria is facing one of its darkest hours! Princess Argent's Mega Shadow minions have been defeated, but the Queen of Fear herself has been blasting the portal with dark magic in an effort to break through. Her army of soldiers and spirits stands ready to sweep through and invade Ponyville! The only way to close the portal is for Summer to overcome her fear of Princess Argent, but she is going to take some convincing! Things do not look good. With the Mane Six using all their power to try and negate Princess Argent's magic, it will be up to the PCs to save Equestria!

To close the portal, they need to get Summer to face and overcome her fears of Nightmare Moon and Princess Argent, something she can only do by facing them. As you might imagine, she is anything but keen to do that. After being talked out of the library she'll follow the PCs to the portal to do her best to help. But the sight of Princess Argent through the mirror, glowing with power and dark energy will prove too much. She will once more run to the corner of the room and sit shivering in terror.

The PCs will have to find a way to help Summer be brave. The best way to do this is to tell her a story about how they managed to face their fears and felt better for doing so. Each PC can take turns in telling Summer such a story. The player might make one up that relates to an experience their character had. But the easiest option is to think back about how they gained any fear points they acquired and turn that into a story of overcoming fear. After all, even though they were frightened, they got this far!

Convincing Summer to step through the portal to face Princess Argent is a Charm test (Difficulty 8). Each PC can make such a test once they have told Summer their story. However, each tale has an effect. Even if the test fails, the difficulty is reduced by 1 for each story the PCs tell Summer. If one of them succeeds, Summer decides she has to be brave for the sake of Equestria and steps forward toward the portal. But he is still clearly terrified and won't go through unless the PCs come with her.

Running the Conclusion

While the way to solve the adventure is for Summer to face Princess Argent, the climax should still be about the PCs. It is they who will convince her to make a stand so the focus should be on their efforts to do that.

When Princess Solar and the Hooves of Light attack Princess Argent, they are not arriving to save the day. All they are doing is buying the group some time to help Summer. The game master should describe how it is going as the PCs try to convince Summer to let go of her fear, making it clear they do not have long. Ideally Princess Argent will be about to rally and finally destroy her enemies just before Summer finds her voice, but that will be tricky to time right!

During the whole scene the game master should play up the lack of time and desperate straits to increase the tension. If they fail here, the army will invade Equestria, and if they take too long, Princess Solar and her forces will suffer a defeat they may not come back from, leaving no one to challenge Princess Argent ever again!

Challenging Princess Argent

As the PCs and Summer step through, Princess Argent will smile with glee. It seems there will be some form of entertainment before she crushes the forces of Equestria! She stops firing energy at the portal and tells her army to stay back. Drawing herself up with regal bearing, she demands to know how a foal and the PCs dare to imagine they might face her, and then she laughs heartily at them for their temerity. Summer screws up her face as she prepares to tell her she isn't afraid, and then, nothing. She balks. Seeing Princess Argent in all her glory is too much and she curls up into a ball, too frightened to even run away. Princess Argent smiles greedily and prepares to order her soldiers to destroy the PCs.

But just before she can order the assault, the sound of a hunting horn echoes through the air. It's the Hooves of Light! Led by Princess Solar, they mount a surprise attack on Princess Argent's army, scattering her soldiers and causing chaos. Princess Solar herself takes on the Queen of Fear. But as an epic battle begins, it is clear to anyone watching that it is a battle Solar cannot win. Princess Argent is too powerful, and the Hooves of Light are too few. But they have bought the PCs time.

Once more the PCs need to get Summer to finally face her fears. It will take Charm tests again (and probably a few Friendship Tokens!) to do so. As before, they will need to tell her how facing her fears won't be as bad as she thinks, and how Princess Argent isn't as bad as she might appear. They might also show her how Princess Solar is overcoming her own fears and doing well, or how good it is not to be ruled by fear, or a bully. They can tell her that it is not about being stronger than Princess Argent, but being stronger than her fear of her.

As before, each PC should have a chance to inspire Summer with a story or words of encouragement. They need to make a Charm test with a Difficulty of 10, but each attempt reduces this by 1. But with each passing round, Princess Argent begins to turn the tide of the battle against her sister!

As soon as one of the PCs convinces Summer to stand up for herself, it is like a floodgate has opened. She stands up, and shouts at Princess Argent (albeit in a squeaky and terrified voice) that she is done being afraid.

As soon as she does, she suddenly gets all of Princess Argent's attention, and something seems to shift in the air around the battle. Summer clearly feels it too and bellows with more confidence that she won't be afraid of a bully anymore!

Her fear falls away, and anyone with magical skill will feel the energy in the area shift like a tidal wave. Princess Argent feels it too. The loss of Summer's fear is a staggering blow to her power, and Princess Solar uses the opportunity to double down on her attacks. Another wave of energy sweeps out of the portal as Summer's fear releases the locks holding it open. From the other side the PCs can see the Mane Six shouting to them to run back so they can close it!

There is only one problem: Summer now doesn't want to leave! The rush of throwing off her fear, and the sight of Princess Argent falling to her knees as she takes her power has rather excited her. She stands there, shouting that she will never be afraid of her again, that she is nothing but a bully and that the only thing she had was what she took from her! Princess Solar will shout to the PCs to leave if they haven't figured out it is time to go already, but they shouldn't leave Summer behind.

There are three ways to get Summer to leave. They can try to convince her to go (Charm test, Difficulty 8) point out that the work is done and they need to go (Mind test, Difficulty 6) or just pick her up and run to the portal (Body test, Difficulty 4)!

If the PCs enjoy scuffles and combat, the game master can put a soldier for each of them between them and the portal, who must be defeated before they can escape. Otherwise it is a straight run to escape the Shadow Realm.

Once they are all through, Twilight Sparkle will begin closing the portal, which gradually turns into a mirror once more. As they watch, Princess Solar sounds the retreat with a wave of thanks to the ponies of Equestria. The final battle between her and Princess Argent may come someday, but this is not that day. The forces of good in the Shadow Realm retreat to regroup and fight another day as the army of evil scatters in confusion. In the middle of all the chaos, Princess Argent howls in rage at being so defeated so close to victory. After all that excitement, everypony can collapse in a heap and be very glad it is finally all over!

Epilogue

When the dust has settled, the PCs and the Mane Six have time to pick themselves up and dust themselves off. The spirits are gone and Equestria is saved! The Mane Six will thank the PCs for everything they have done. Summer will be exhausted and will only just have time to thank them too before she falls asleep.

Each of the PCs can gain a well learned level from the whole affair. They can also heal and remove all their fear points. In addition, they have earned the trust and favor of the Mane Six, who may call on them to help in their adventures again, probably quite soon!

Further Adventures

While the PC's adventures in the Shadow Realm have come to an end for now, it may not be the last they have heard of Princess Argent. The Queen of Fear now knows about Nightmare Moon and is desperate to claim the helm Princess Luna made to transform herself. She will stop at nothing to find another way into Equestria.

However, this time she will be more careful. While the portal mirror will be taken away by Princess Celestia and locked away securely, there may be other mirrors out there. With powerful magic at her command, Princess Argent may find another way to break through, although this time she will be subtle. She might send a few secret spies to look for the helm before she tries to come into Equestria herself. She might even try to swap places with Princess Luna to trick Princess Celestia into helping her.

But further adventures might not involve Princess Argent looking to get into Equestria. The PCs may wonder what Princess Solar is up to and want to help her rebellion against the Queen of Fear. They may just want to know that she and the Hooves of Light are okay after the battle. They will have to find another portal to do that, and while Princess Solar will be very glad to see them, opening another portal may have inadvertently given Princess Argent another way to invade Equestria!

If the PCs enjoyed meeting the ghostly spirits, not all of them might have returned home. Many don't like Princess Argent, and some are just fascinated with Equestria. They might cause all manner of trouble, possibly out of a sense of mischief or just ignorance of what sort of behavior is expected of them. Either way, they will need to be dealt with by the PCs. But if some of them want to stay and are prepared to behave properly, they will need someone to speak on their behalf to Princess Celestia so they are allowed to stay.

Finally, there are many other mirrors and many other worlds to explore. The PCs might visit any number of strange new places and mysterious alternate realities. Princess Celestia won't like the idea, as she knows what can go wrong, but then, nopony has to tell her...

The game master can have a lot of fun creating new worlds. Many will be just like Equestria, but with a subtle difference. Some possibilities are:

★ A world where Nightmare Moon never returned to being Princess Luna.

★ A place the Mane Six never met and discovered the Elements of Harmony.

★ An Equestria where King Sombra took charge of the whole land.

★ A place where Changelings remain undetected and have replaced several prominent characters.

★ A world where the Cutie Mark Crusaders were the ones to discover the Elements of Harmony and become the heroes of Equestria instead.

★ A land where Unicorns, Pegasi, and Earth ponies never learned to get along, where the Windigos have transformed Equestria into a frozen wasteland.

Also, just as you might create alternate version of Equestria, the new worlds might be created from completely different genres, allowing the PCs to go to even more outlandish and strange places, such as:

★ An industrial revolution era Ponyville where Fetlock Holmes solves crime on the smog covered streets.

★ Space Station Ponyville, a huge orbital trading post in the heart of Equestrian space where the ponies explore strange new worlds.

★ A Wild West where the frontier town of Ponyville is besieged by bandits and crooked land barons.

★ Castle Ponyville, where great knights battle evil dragons with a help of one of Star Swirl the Bearded's students called Merlin.

★ The Chateau Pony De Ville where musketeers protect the honor of their king and swing on an awful lot of chandeliers.

And there's more!

Keep exploring Equestria and enjoying your adventures with our range of useful gaming aids and expansion books for *Tails of Equestria*. Note that some of the artwork shown here may vary when production is finalized.

Tails of Equestria: Starter Set

The Starter Set is the perfect way for beginners to start playing Tails of Equestria. 'A Dragon's Bounty' is an adventure book that can be played solo by simply reading the book. Players can build their own adventure by choosing which paths to take and how to confront each challenge, telling their own story along the way. This Starter Set does not require a Gamemaster, so getting started has never been quicker and easier for new players.

Expansion Books

These supplements are vital guides and collections of information for the GM and the players alike. The first example of these is *The Bestiary of Equestria*—a source of knowledge about the many creatures and races that inhabit the magical land of Equestria.

Adventures

Each of these books gives you a new story and all the details the GM is going to need to run a fun and challenging adventure. The first one can be found in *The Curse of the Statuettes expansion set*, which also includes a pad of **Pony Sheets**, a set of **roleplaying dice**, and a **GM screen** – the screen allows the GM to keep all information that the players cannot see (yet) secret. It also includes core information for quick reference.

Build a Campaign

The Festival of Lights and *Judge Not by the Cover* are the next two adventures in our line, suiting PCs of different levels and experience. Each can be played separately, or you can play all three adventures in a row, creating a longer campaign story!

PONY SHEET

Character Name: ....

Player Name: ....

Pony Type: ....

Level: ....

Element of Harmony: ....

Friendship

Stamina:

Max ....

Current ....

Body

Mind

Charm

Talents

CM:..

T:..

T:..

T:..

T:..

Portrait

Quirks

Main:..

Q:..

Q:..

Q:..

Cutie Mark

RIVER HORSE